I STINK!

I STINK!

KATE & JIM McMULLAN

SCHOLASTIC INC.
New York Toronto London Auckland Sydney
Mexico City New Delhi Hong Kong Buenos Aires

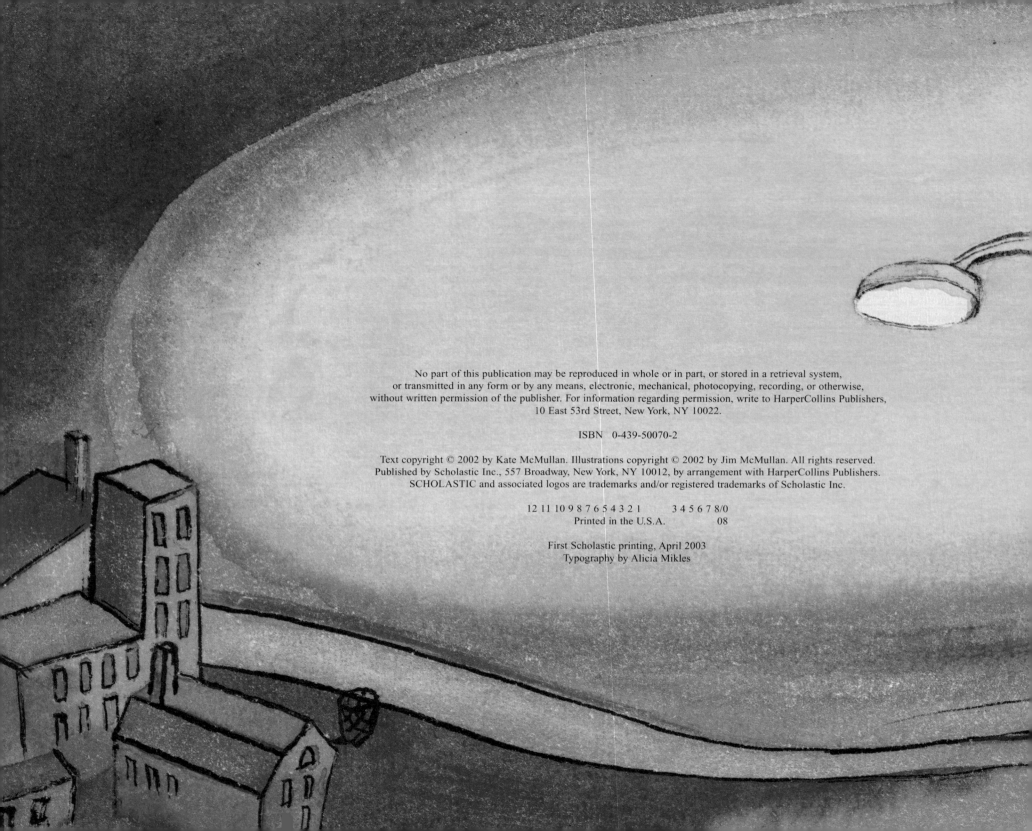

ISBN   0-439-50070-2

12 11 10 9 8 7 6 5 4 3 2 1   3 4 5 6 7 8/0
Printed in the U.S.A.   08

First Scholastic printing, April 2003
Typography by Alicia Mikles

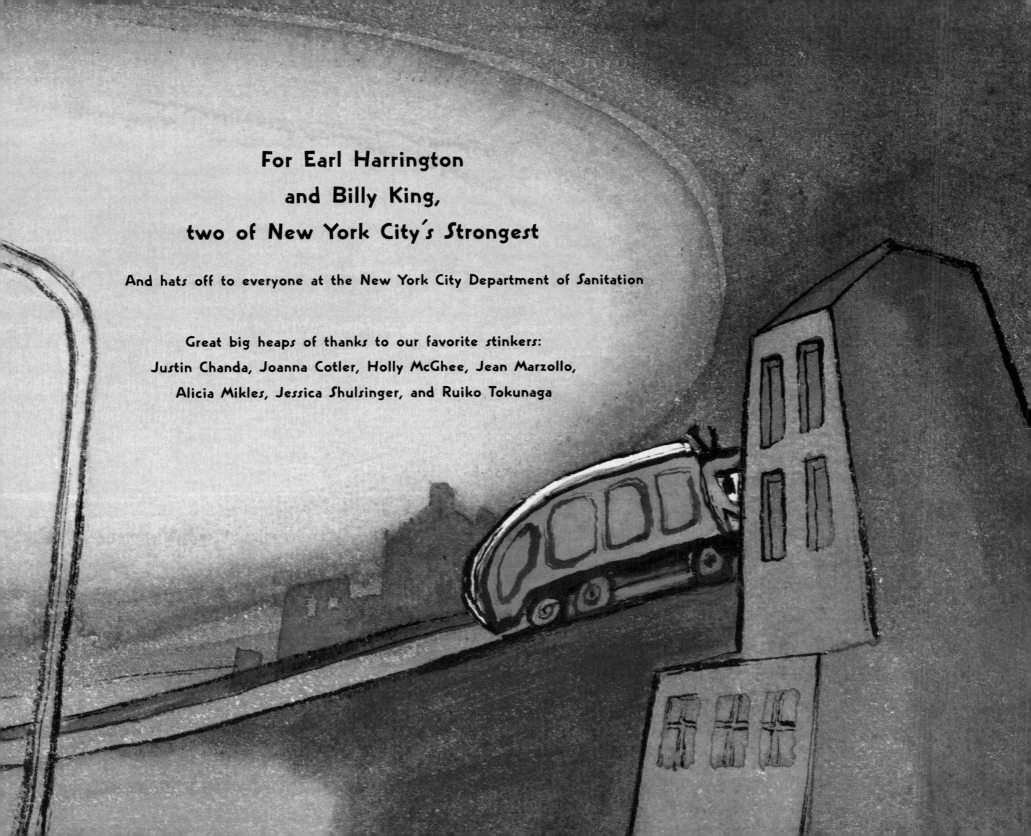

For Earl Harrington
and Billy King,
two of New York City's Strongest

And hats off to everyone at the New York City Department of Sanitation

Great big heaps of thanks to our favorite stinkers:
Justin Chanda, Joanna Cotler, Holly McGhee, Jean Marzollo,
Alicia Mikles, Jessica Shulsinger, and Ruiko Tokunaga

Who am I? I've got lights.
Ten **WIDE** tires.
No A.C., not me.
I've got doubles:
steering wheels,
gas pedals,
brakes.
I am totally **DUAL OP.**
Know what I do at night
while you're asleep?

Feed me!

Straight into my HOPPER!

Nice toss, guys!

STOP!

Hopper's full.
Hit the **THROTTLE**.

Gimme some gas.
Rev me to the

MAX.

Engine?

ROAR!

Did I wake you?
Too bad!

PISTONS?

Bring on the crusher blade.

BLADE?

Push back the BAGS.

SQUEEZE them!

Crush them!

Mash them!

Smash them!

Whoa, those bags are

WAY
COMPACTED.

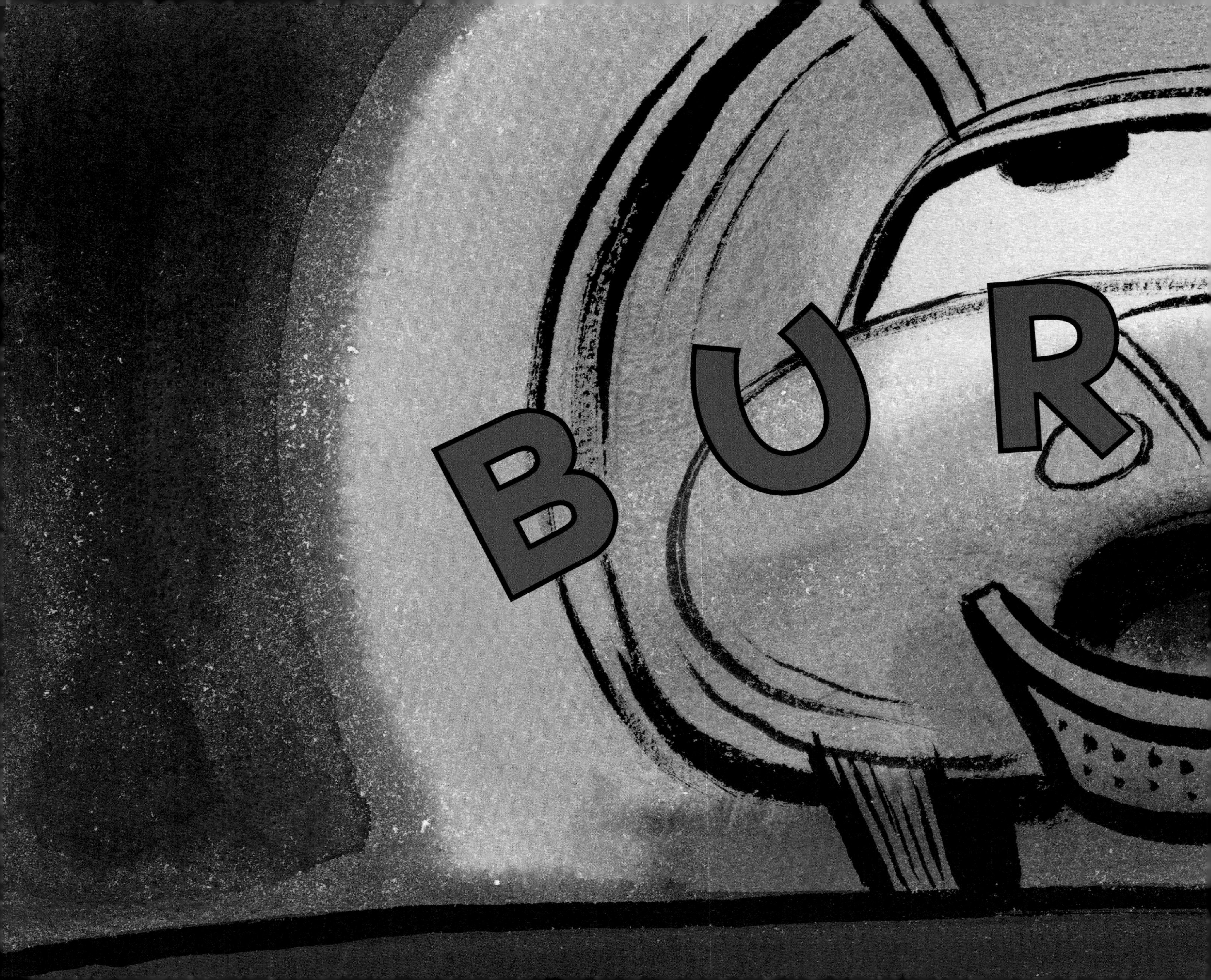
BUR

Ahhhhhh!
NOW I HAVE ROOM FOR ALPHABET SOUP.
Get a LOAD of my recipe:

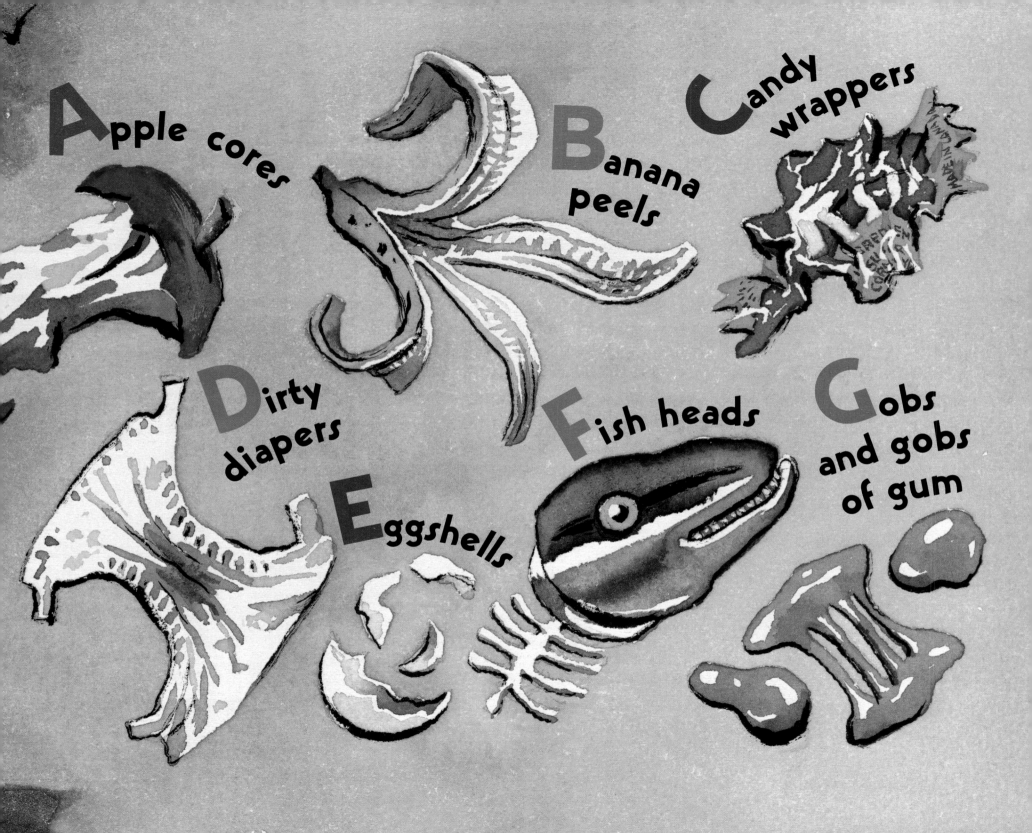

Half-eaten hot dogs

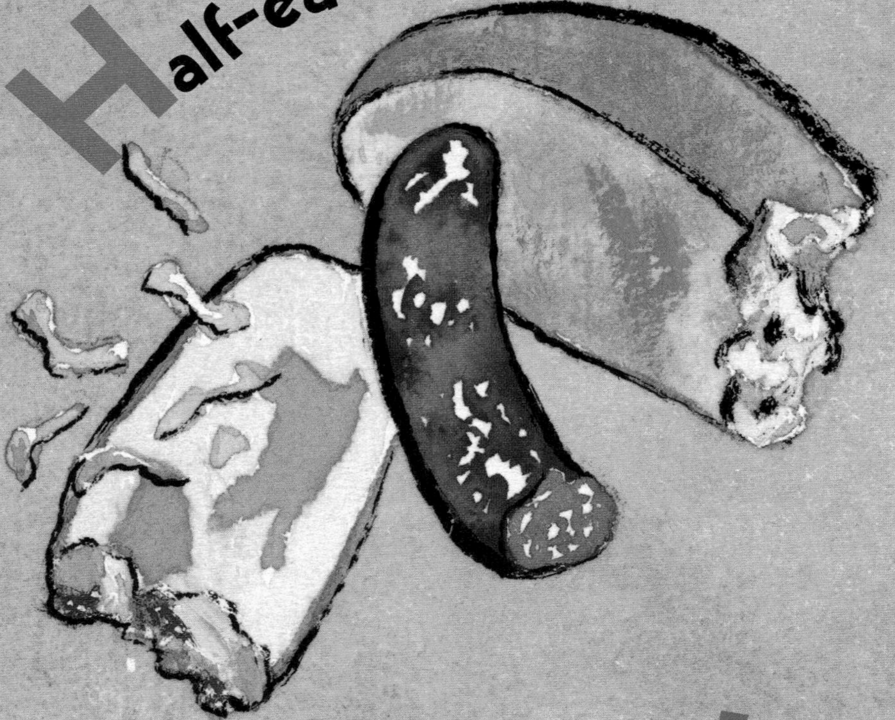

Icky ice cream cartons

Jam jars

Kitty litter

Lobster claws

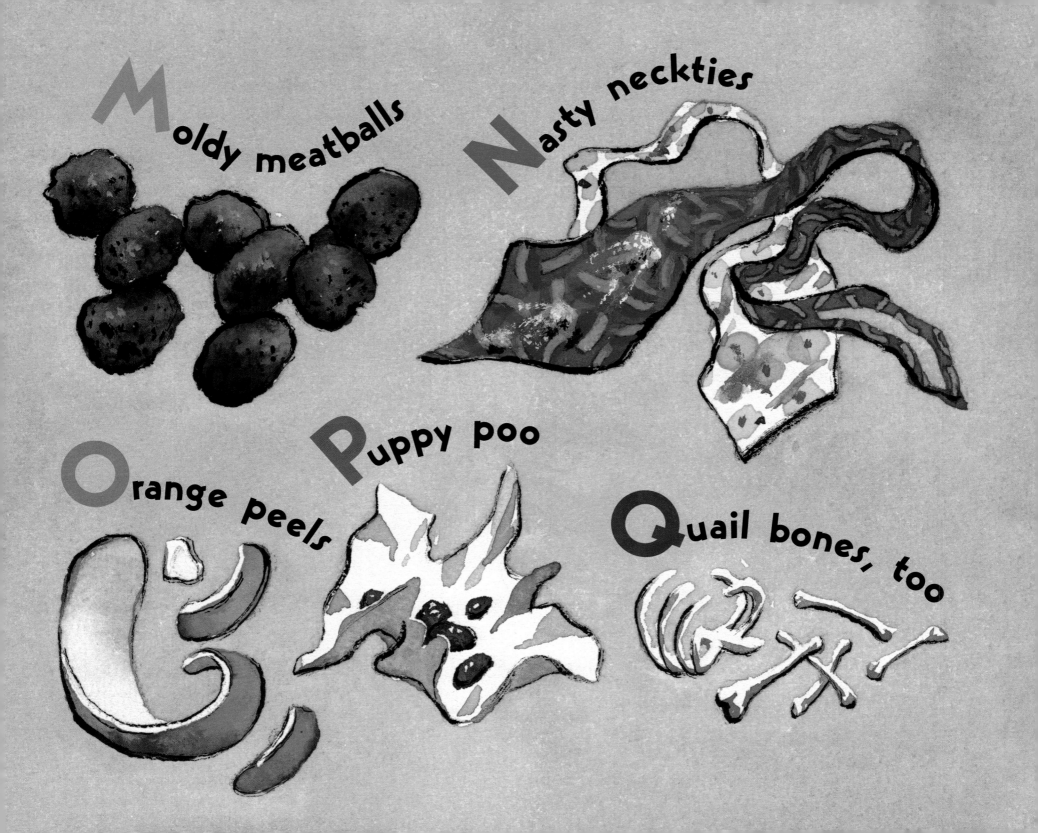

Moldy meatballs

Nasty neckties

Orange peels

Puppy poo

Quail bones, too

Rotten radishes **S**melly sneakers **T**oothpaste tubes

Ugly underpants **V**acuum bags

Watermelon rinds

XL T-shirts

Year-old yams

Zipped-up ziti with zucchini

NEXT STOP, THE RIVER.

Lights?
FLASH!
Driver?
REVERSE!

Get me to the barge.

Hear me blast my

BACK-UP RAP:

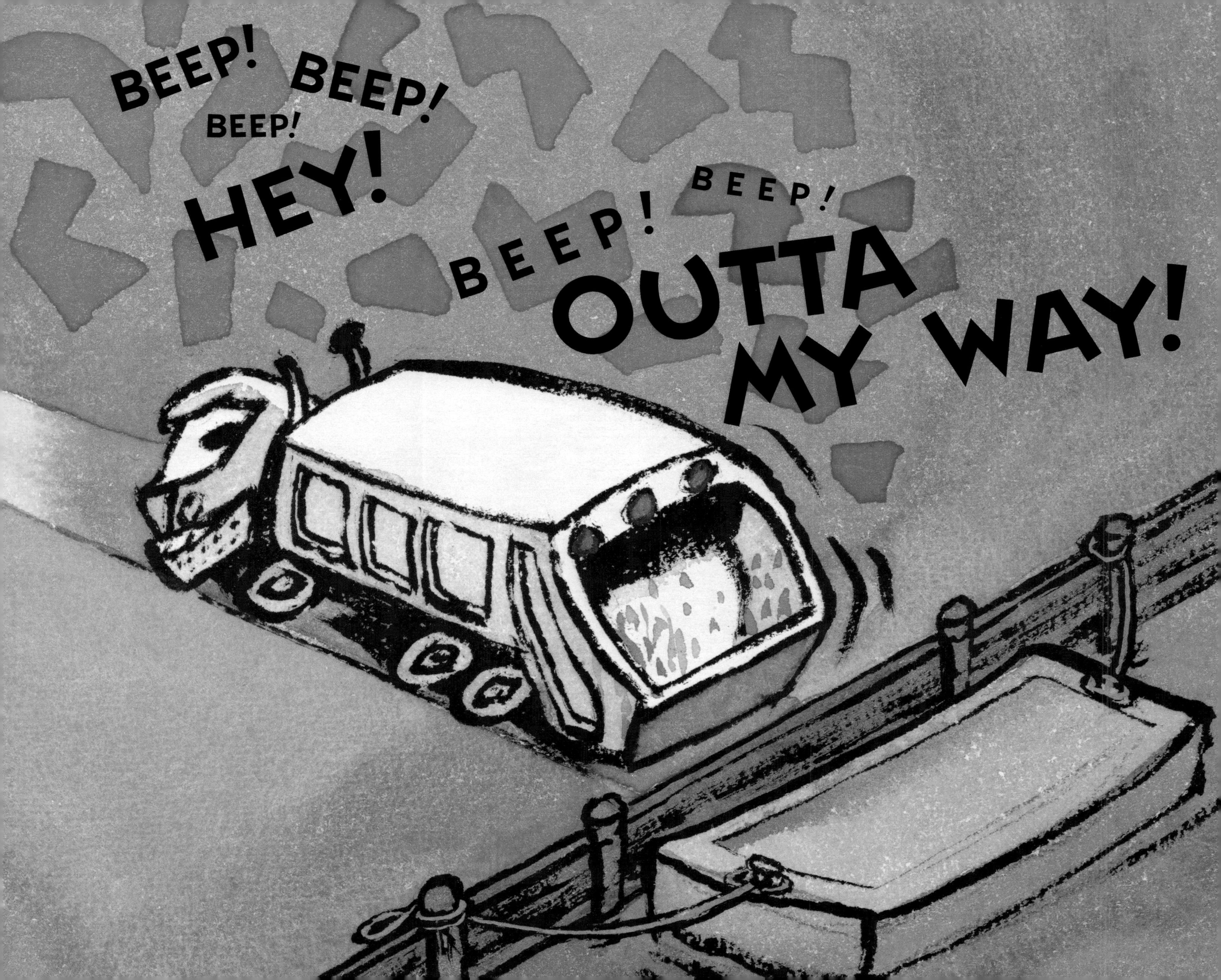
BEEP! BEEP!
BEEP!
HEY!
BEEP! BEEP!
OUTTA MY WAY!

Ready, crew . . .
ACTION!

Pins?
OUT!

Power take-off switch?
HIT IT!

Tail gate?
SEPARATE!

Up, up, up!

Tail-gate sweeper?

EJECT!

PLOP!

Who am I?

THE GARBAGE TRUCK,